CW00401026

Star Quality

with Alvin the Performing Bear

First published 2004 by Pan Macmillan Ltd

Pan Macmillan, 20 New Wharf Road, London N1 9RR

Basingstoke and Oxford

Associated companies throughout the world

www.panmacmillan.com

ISBN 0 7522 1570 1

A CIP catalogue record for this book is available from the British Library.

Design by Dan Newman @ Perfect Bound Ltd

Text by Natalie Jerome

Colour Reproduction by Aylesbury Studios Ltd.

Printed by Proost, Belgium

Aardman presents

Star Quality

with Alvin the Performing Bear

'I haven't got any circus skills at all. I can't juggle, I can't throw the knife at the lady, I can't tame the lion and I can't crack the whip or jump into the small bucket. I can't do any of those things.'

angus h. wintergarden

"The thing that excites me about performing is that it's a release of any tensions that you might have inside you."

miss dynamite

'You'd think after all this time I wouldn't, but yes I still do – I still FREAK OUT and PANIC and fear the audience reaction to me. And then I get over it.'

'I had to stand on one leg and do a raspberry. Go arse over whatsit in front of 250 people And I bonked my head – I thought I was a gonna. And I heard them as I hit the floor go 'oooohh' like that and it was weird cos I took off. I just flew. And I was so embarrassed. I was like 'No I'm fine, I'm fine. Just get back on, get back on. I'm back, I'm back.'

matilda

muzulu & toto

'The thing that excites me really about performing is the fact that you are doing something good, you're making people laugh.'

'Except for the ones that walk off.'

'You need to warm up all those areas of the body, then move on to your voice and I start to hum — hmmm. It opens up your voice, it relaxes and strengthens your vocal chords It warms everything up.'

'Apart from doing a bit of stretching, a bit of yoga, trying to get my foot behind my neck, and stuff like that, we used to get down and do 20 — "drop and give me 20" — give it loads of bravadery, kind of y'know, blokey business.'

'I can't even juggle.'
'Neither can I.
I can juggle with two
things, but not with three.'
'That's not really juggling,
is it?'

'No, it's chucking stuff up
into the air, isn't it?'
'Yeah.'

muzulu & toto

"We spent a huge amount of time when we're on the road exercising, we would stay up all night long practising our handstands. We used to spend hours balancing and tumbling and helping each other learn tricks."

'I was doing a job in Brighton recently and that had a real buzz about it and then I was in Suffolk or somewhere like that, doing an agricultural show and people had come to look at the cows.'

'You've got to communicate with the audience but not to look at them, because you are apart from them and it will break the illusion.'

angus h. wintergarden

fluffy

'Clowns are just creepy, aren't they? They're not funny at all. They're just weird.'

muzulu & toto

'One of the things we least like about what we do is working with each other. You're constantly having to travel with each other, work with each other, be creative, do interviews, do everything together.'

'If there aren't a few butterflies around in the tummy before you go on stage, you're probably not going to give a good performance. You've got to be keyed up.'

angus h. wintergarden

mr tickles

'You feel sick sometimes but as soon as I go onstage I think – well this is it, I can't turn back now, I'm on, I'm on, I'm on – oh God, there comes the lights, the lights are going up. Inside the real me is saying 'oh my God, oh my God, here we go, why am I doing this, I love it when I'm doing it, I know I love it when I'm doing it, but why am I doing it – I'm glad I didn't have too much to eat.'

'I am scared of heights, yes, but I think I can get over it.'

wilhelm II & titania

'I normally try and interact with an audience but with 800 it becomes really difficult. But I actually think I managed and that's an amazing feeling, to just see that you're making an impact.'

'We did a show a couple of years ago. 8,000 kids saw it in a week, we had about 1,000 kids per performance. And the kids were like 8 or 9 screaming blue murder. Oh I have never been so scared in all my life. Why do I do it, I must be stupid. And you get out there and you look out and you think, they're just loving it and they're completely engrossed in what you're doing.'

muzulu & toto

'We turned down Freddie Star didn't we?'
'We turned down Freddie Star.'
'He couldn't pay enough for us.'
'That was the highlight of our career I think.'
'That was the highlight of our career, turning down Freddie Star.'

'Every time I went on I could just feel the people laughing at me. It was fantastic. That gives me such a buzz, such a hell of a buzz.'

Mr Roger's Magical Orchestra

mr tickles

"That's something I hadn't really considered, appearing on television. But if the chance came, yes Yes it would be a new dimension."

angus h. wintergarden